Kroučilová .

A QUARTO BOOK

First published in Canada in 1984 by
Prentice-Hall Canada, Inc.
Scarborough, Ontario

Canadian Cataloguing in Publication Data
Niering, William A.
A book of wildflowers
ISBN 0-13-080094-5
1. Wild flowers.   I. Title.
QK85.5.N53 1984   582.13   C83-098916-1

A Book of Wildflowers
was produced and prepared by
Quarto Marketing Ltd.
212 Fifth Avenue, New York, NY 10010

Editor: **Bill Logan**
Art Director/Designer: **Richard Boddy**

Typeset by BPE Graphics, Inc.
Color separations by
Hong Kong Scanner Craft Company Ltd.
Printed and bound in Hong Kong by
Leefung-Asco Printers Ltd.

CONTENTS

This beautifully illustrated volume is dedicated to my wife, Catherine, and to my students who have shared my interest in the botanical world.

INTRODUCTION

This wildflower sampler is different from other such books in that it includes mostly species which occur in both North America and Europe. This does not imply that these plants have naturally evolved over this wide range but rather that man has played an integral part as disseminator. As Old World peoples migrated from Europe to the New World, the seeds of many of these species were inadvertently brought as contaminants in crop seed or in straw packing. These alien seeds found crop land and clearings ideal for their establishment and propagation. One need only walk into an untended vegetable garden or old field which has recently been agriculturally abandoned to attest to the success of these migrants. In my garden, celandine, black-eyed Susans and buttercups are frequent "weeds," and in that part of my lawn which I have allowed to grow into an unmowed, grassy meadow, daisies, yarrow and hawkweeds all thrive and add splashes of color throughout the summer.

Although most, if not all, of the wildflowers included here are really quite beautiful, as revealed by the superb artistry of Anita Marci, about half of them are considered weeds and are controlled by cultivation or herbicides where they occur in agriculture. This raises a most interesting question— what is a weed? It has been variously defined. Ralph Waldo Emerson suggested that it is a plant whose virtues have yet to be discovered. Others consider it a plant out of place. Queen Anne's Lace, blueweed and chickory would be colorful wildflowers in my meadow, but in a pasture or crop land they would be considered weeds.

Many weeds are highly cosmopolitan. For example, blueweed occurs commonly as a plant of clearings or open fields and pastures in North America, Europe and Australia. Typically, weeds are opportunistic species in that they take advantage of open disturbed sites where they do not have to compete too heavily with other species for space, sun, and water. They seldom threaten well-stabilized ecosystems within a given area. Some, however, like purple loosestrife, compete seriously with the native wetland flora in parts of North America. Man has not only played a major role in the geographical distribution of many of these plants, he has also helped to favor their continued occurrence.

Most of these wildflowers are perennials which means that once established, they will automatically come up from year to year from the persisting root systems. Some others are biennials like celandine, mullein and evening primrose which form a rosette of basal leaves the first year followed by flowering and seed production in the second year after which the plant's roots die. A few like hare's foot clover are annuals which respond like the marigolds in our ornamental gardens. They must be started from seed each year and complete their life cycle in one year.

In addition to beautiful "weeds," this volume also includes some truly spectacular wildflowers such as orchids, irises, lilies and columbines. These often occur as woodland spring wildflowers. Early flowering is a marvelous adaptation for taking advantge of the light available in spring before the forest canopy closes over for the summer.

Among the 55 species in this primer, the pea and daisy families are best represented. Members of the pea family are ecologically important as nitrogen fixers. Their roots have the ability to take nitrogen from the soil and convert it into a usable source of nitrogen for the plant. When the plant dies, the soil is further enriched with nitrogen. The daisy family, one of the largest with over 20,000 species, has been most successful. This may be correlated with its highly evolved flower. Members of this family produce their flowers in heads in which many tiny florets are aggregated closely together so that when insect pollinators land many flowers are simultaneously pollinated. The tiny fruits or seeds of most of these flowers are dispersed as minute "parachutes" of fine bristles on wind currents.

As you enjoy this volume remember that this is but a sample of the more than 250,000 species of flowering plants that have evolved on our planet. Many of those included here may be just outside your door, even in an urban setting. May this be the beginning of an outdoor adventure that will lead to many hours of enjoyment searching for and identifying wildflowers.

William A. Niering

ACHILLEA

YARROW

(A. millefolium)

(Family: *Asteraceae*)

❧

This is a pleasant aromatic plant with very striking
fern-like leaves. The whitish-gray, flat-topped flower
clusters are composed of many separate
flowers—yellowish central ones and whitish outer
ones. The plant has been used in folk medicine to
stop bleeding and tea brewed from its leaves is said
to remedy colds. It is typically found along roadsides,
in open fields and in pastures. A closely related pink
form, *A. lanulosa,* is planted in American gardens as
an ornamental.

ALLIUM

WILD GARLIC
FIELD GARLIC
(A. vineale)
(Family: *Liliaceae*)

~

The small flowers of wild garlic are structurally
similar to those of the large showy daylilies found in
ornamental gardens, but they are less conspicuous.
Wild garlic is related to the garden onion, and its
bulb has a distinct garlic taste. In fact, if it becomes
too abundant in low pastures or wheat fields, an
undesirable taste is imparted to the resulting milk
or flour. Found throughout the United States,
it is considered an exotic pest, especially
in the southeast.

AQUILEGIA

COLUMBINE
(A. canadensis)
(Family: *Ranunculaceae*)

～

Columbine is a beautiful woodland flower found on
rocky slopes and ledges. The five petals of the
blossom form long spurs so that only long-tongued
butterflies and moths can collect the sweet nectar
within. Related to the common garden columbine, it
is widely distributed in the eastern half of the United
States, also extending into Canada, as the species
name implies. Walking among the woodland
boulders of New England in Spring, one observer
commented, "Every nook and cranny among them,
and every little mat of earth upon them, is checkered
with the flowery print of the Canada columbine."

CALLA

WATER ARUM
WILD CALLA
(C. palustris)
(Family: *Araceae*)

The beautiful white or whitish-green leaf-like
structure (the spathe) of the calla envelopes a golden
club (the spadix) with tiny female flowers crowded at
the base and usually male flowers toward the tip.
The fruiting head consists of red berry-like clusters.
Indians and early European settlers in America used
the roots to make a type of flour. This plant is
related to skunk cabbage and jack-in-the-pulpit
and like them, is frequently found in swampy
and boggy areas.

CAMPANULA

HAREBELL
BLUEBELL
(C. rotundifolia)
(Family: *Campanulaceae*)

Lovely, nodding, bell-like flowers on thread-like stalks
distinguish this member of the bluebell family.
Bumblebees are among the chief pollinators, and
they must clasp the stigma of the inverted flower to
enter, thus facilitating pollination. Campanula can be
found on rocky banks, in meadows and near shores.
At high elevations it may have but a single flower.

CHELIDONIUM

CELANDINE
(C. majus)
(Family: *Papaveraceae*)

~

The highly ornamental leaves of this delicate annual
make it an attractive filler around the edges of the
flower garden. However, it can be rather aggressive.
A member of the poppy family, it displays a bright
orange juice when the foliage or stems are bruised.
The juice has been used in folk medicine for liver
disorders and also for removal of warts and freckles.

CHRYSANTHEMUM

OX-EYE DAISY
(C. leucanthemum)
(Family: *Asteraceae*)

~

You may be surprised to learn that this daisy is a
Chrysanthemum related to the huge mums sold in
flower shops. Typical of open clearings, they are
among the showiest members of the daisy family.
The flower head is a composite of flowers consisting
of many individuals. Those tightly packed in the
center form a "button" and are tube-shaped,
whereas white strap-like flowers—petal-like in
appearance—surround the yellow disk. The
ornamentally lobed leaves also help to distinguish
this old field wildflower.

CICHORIUM

CHICORY
SUCCORY
(C. intybus)
(Family: *Asteraceae*)

Chicory is a very beautiful roadside perennial with
striking, true violet-blue blooms—a shade not
common among flowers. These close in the rain but
open in full sun. Five distinctive points at the end of
each strap represent five fused petals, the corolla.
The many individual strap-like corollas that
comprise each flower head are fascinating to study
closely. Five fused stamens and a pistil are also
present on each strap, making each a complete
flower. The long taproot is dried and added to coffee
to improve the flavor.

CORNUS

DWARF CORNEL
BUNCHBERRY
(C. canadensis)
(Family: *Cornaceae*)

This dainty wildflower of the northern forests can be
found across southern Canada to Labrador. It is a
dwarf member of the dogwood family with four
white petal-like bracts which surround a cluster of
tiny flowers. By late August, a compact cluster of
scarlet berries appears. This species and *C. suecica,*
which is also found in the north woods, are the only
soft bushes in this predominantly woody family.

CORONILLA

CROWN VETCH
AXSEED
(C. varia)
(Family: *Fabaceae*)

~

    Clusters of flowers similar to those of sweet peas make this an especially showy plant which is often found planted along roadsides to stabilize newly graded slopes. As a legume it can make its own nitrogenous compounds from the atmospheric nitrogen found in the soil, and through this process it improves soil fertility. The genus name *Coronilla* comes from the fact that the plants have been used to make wreaths and garlands since ancient times.

CYPRIPEDIUM

YELLOW LADY'S-SLIPPER

LADY'S-SLIPPER ORCHID

(C. calceolus)

(Family: *Orchidaceae*)

The Latin name meaning "little shoe" is very appropriate, if a bit plain, for this showy orchid with a distinctive yellow sac forming one of its petals. The other two petals are brownish and spirally elongated.

The Indians used the root in the treatment of parasitic worms. It grows in woods, thickets, bogs and swamps. Cypripedium is a fine choice for the wild or bog garden.

Cytissus

BROOM

(C. scoparius)

(Family: *Fabaceae*)

Covered with golden yellow, pea-like blossoms, this erect stiff-stemmed shrub can reach 8 feet (2.5 m) in height. Its small leaves often fall, leaving the green stems bare. It is widespread in Europe where it can be found on heaths and in woodland clearings. A drug made from the twigs is used for heart and respiratory ailments although the plant itself is poisonous to livestock. Branches are used for brooms, the plant having given its name to that housekeeping tool. It can coat whole landscapes with its yellow spikes. This is the flower that Wordsworth said "along the copses runs in veins of gold."

DAUCUS

QUEEN-ANNE'S LACE
WILD CARROT
(D. carota)
(Family: *Apiaeae*)

~

This lacy, flat-topped flower cluster rivals any queen's lace in texture and beauty. Often there is a single, large, reddish-purple flower in the center. It thrives in open fields or exposed ground. This hairy biennial was the ancestor of the garden carrot; its first-year taproot can be cooked and eaten. Although considered a weed, it is a most attractive addition to the informal, naturalistic garden.

DIANTHUS

DEPTFORD PINK
(D. armeria)
(Family: *Caryophyllaceae*)

~

This flower with its five delicate, jagged-edged petals resembles the garden flower Sweet William. The common name refers to Deptford, England, now a part of London, where the plant was once abundant. You can find this deep pink flower in fields or along hedgerows and roadsides. It is also called Lady's Cushion or Thrift.

DIGITALIS

FOXGLOVE
(D. purpurea)
(Family: *Scrophulariaceae*)

~

The nodding bell-shaped blossoms of this plant are
especially ornamental. The Latin name refers to the
finger-like flowers. Although grown in gardens,
foxglove frequently escapes into the wild and is
widely distributed in temperate regions of the world.
In New Zealand I have even seen them growing wild
along the coast near Nelson. An important drug,
digitalin, obtained from the leaves, is used to slow
down the rate of heart beat. It is a difficult medicinal
plant, though, as slightly too large a dose can
prove deadly poison.

Echium

Viper's Bugloss
Blueweed
(E. vulgare)
(Family: *Boraginaceae*)

The common name bugloss comes from the Greek *bouglossos* meaning "ox-tongued" and refers to the roughness of the leaves. This plant has been used in folk medicine for the treatment of snakebite. Each of the vase-like flowers has four long red stamens protruding beyond the blue petals. It is thought to have been introduced into North America from Europe as early as 1683. Although the blossoms are attractive, farmers often call it Blue Devil, since it grows rampantly in their fields. In Australia it often forms a sea of blue in sheep paddocks.

EPILOBIUM

FIREWEED
WILLOW-HERB
ROSEBAY
(E. angustifolium)
(Family: *Onagraceae*)

～

Fireweed's flowers are distinctively four-parted, and the ovary gives rise to an attractive, long and slender fruit. When ripe, these fruits split open and discharge large numbers of seeds with silky parachutes which can be carried long distances by the wind. Fireweed is often the first plant to colonize burn sites, transforming the blackened landscape into a sea of pink.

EPIPACTIS

BROAD HELLEBORINE
(E. helleborine)
(Family: *Orchidaceae*)

This is a large orchid reaching 4 feet (1.2 meters) in height. Its drooping, scentless flowers tend to occur along one side of the flowering stalk. Individual blossoms with their little sac-like lips merit close examination. The large, spirally arranged leaves have conspicuous veins and are often over 6 inches (15 cm) in length. Found in woods and thickets and along streamsides, this is the only orchid known to have been introduced to North America from Europe.

ERODIUM

COMMON STORKSBILL
ALFILARIA
(E. cicutarium)
(Family: *Geraniaceae*)

The plant takes its common names from the long,
beak-like capsules which are its fruits. The leaves
resemble a fern's leaves, and the small, light purple
flowers rise on long stalks in groups of two to nine.
Storksbill is common from early spring to
mid-autumn throughout Great Britain and North
America. In the western United States—where it is
also called by the picturesque names Filaree and
Clocks—it will bloom as early as February. Storksbill
prefers clearings, roadsides, fields and dunes,
growing even in the Sonoran desert of the American
Southwest. Surprisingly, it is a member of the
geranium family.

FILIPENDULA

MEADOWSWEET
QUEEN OF THE MEADOWS
(F. ulmaria)
(Family: *Rosaceae*)

❧

The many small, creamy white flowers of this tall
perennial are arranged in flat-topped clusters, and its
leaves are divided into numerous, separate leaflets.
Found in meadows, swamps and marshes, it is
closely related to the spiraeas of ornamental gardens.
Its flowers have been used in flavoring beverages and
the leaves brewed as an herb tea. Chaucer lists it as
an ingredient in a curative libation called Save, and
it was Queen Elizabeth I's favorite herb for strewing
in her chamber. The great herbalist Gerard said of it,
"The smell thereof makes the heart merry,
delighteth the senses."

GALIUM

YELLOW BEDSTRAW
(G. verum)
(Family: *Rubiaceae*)

This is one of the many bedstraws with tiny flowers and whorls of small leaves that arise from a smooth squarish stem. It was introduced into North America from Europe and is found in dry fields. In medieval times bedstraw was used to fill mattresses, as the common name suggests. Then, it was also called Maid's Hair, for it looked, as one writer put it, "like the loose, un-snooded hair of maidens."

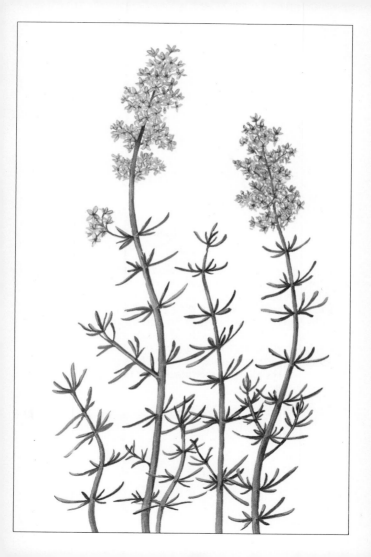

HABENARIA

PURPLE-FRINGED ORCHID
(H. fimbriata)
(Family: *Orchidaceae*)

One of the petals of this orchid is highly modified,
forming a deeply fringed lip, and spurred. Nectar
accumulates in the spur. Butterflies and moths are
the chief pollinators. As they search for nectar, pollen
often gets picked up and carried to another flower.
This is one of the most strikingly beautiful wild
orchids in North America. The purplish lilac flowers
make a gorgeous addition to the bog garden, though
the plant demands a very acid soil.

HIERACIUM

ORANGE HAWKWEED
DEVIL'S PAINTBRUSH
(H. aurantiacum)
(Family: *Asteraceae*)

An expanse of orange hawkweed in bloom along a
roadside or in an open field can be breathtaking. In
spite of its loveliness, however, it is considered a
pernicious weed. The blackish hairs on the bracts
around the flower heads and elsewhere are a
distinctive feature. A sixteenth-century herbalist
indicated that due to the likeness of these hairs to
coal dust, women named the plant Grim the Collier.
Its symmetrical heads are composed solely of
strap-like flowers and arise from a set of basal leaves.

HYPERICUM

COMMON ST. JOHNSWORT
(H. perforatum)
(Family: *Hypericaceae*)

A native of Asia, this plant has become successfully
naturalized in Europe and North America where it is
common in fields and along roadsides. The yellow
flowers, with their numerous stamens, are very
showy. The small, opposite, ovate leaves have
translucent dots visible when held up to the light.
The common name is derived from St. John's
Eve—June 24—when the plant blooms. Folk legends
say the leaves develop red spots on August 29, the
day the saint was beheaded. The suffix wort meant
medicinal herb in Anglo-Saxon, and the plant has
had endless uses in herbal medicine. It was even
supposed to cure madness, though tradition says
that anyone treading on it after dark will be wheeled
through the heavens all night on the back
of a magical horse.

IMPATIENS

ORANGE BALSAM
JEWELWEED
SPOTTED TOUCH-ME-NOT
(I. capensis)
(Family: *Balsaminaceae*)

❧

The plant takes its genus name *Impatiens* from the apparent impatience with which its seed pods burst open, spreading the seeds all around. You can sometimes make the pods open just by touching them, so the plant has also been called Touch-me-not. Impatiens' jewel-like flowers dangle like delicate earrings. The orange blooms are splotched with reddish-brown and are sharply spurred. Its soft stems are translucent, and its leaves give a silvery sheen when placed underwater. The stem juice is used by many to relieve the itching caused by poison ivy. Impatiens is found in shaded wetlands and along creek banks.

IRIS

YELLOW FLAG
(I. pseudacorus)
(Family: *Iridaceae*)

~

Introduced from the Old World to American gardens, this showy iris has escaped from cultivated gardens and is now naturalized in many wetlands. It is also frequently found along river marshes. Sword-like leaves distinguish the members of the iris group. The flowers are unique in form with three backward-curving sepals and three upright petals. Beneath the three arching stigma over the sepals are three hidden stamens. The brown fruits (capsules) may be used in dried flower arrangements. Other local names for it include Dragon Flower, and for its leaves, Dagger Flower.

LAMIUM

HENBIT
(L. amplexicaule)
(Family: *Lamiaceae*)

～

Whorls of rosy-purple, two-lipped flowers encircle the
square stem which bears distinctively scalloped,
opposite leaves. This square stem is characteristic of
the mints. The leaves are tasty when boiled and,
when young, can also be eaten raw. This mint
can be found in fields and cultivated areas
or along roadsides.

LEONURUS

MOTHERWORT
(L. cardiaca)
(Family: *Lamiaceae*)

❧

Small clusters of flowers occur in the axils (bases) of
the leaves of this plant. The opposite wedge-shaped,
three-lobed leaves arise from a square stem typical of
the mints. The scientific species name refers to the
plant's use as a heart stimulant by herbalists. The
common name motherwort stems from its use in folk
medicine for menstrual problems. The Renaissance
herbalist Culpeper contended, "there is no better
herb to take melancholy vapors from the heart, and
to strengthen it; it makes mothers joyful, and
settles the womb."

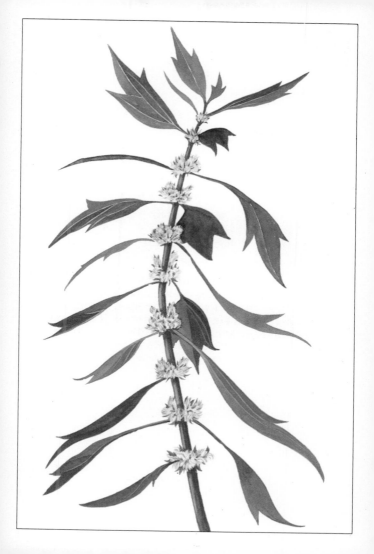

LILIUM

MARTAGON LILY
(L. martagon)
(Family: *Liliaceae*)

The spectacular nodding blossoms occur in clusters of three to ten. The flowers are a flesh-like pink or pale purple, mottled with darker spots. Petals and petal-like sepals are strongly reflexed. It is found throughout Europe in woods and thickets. This is a sequel to the Turk's cap lily, *L. superbum,* found in North America.

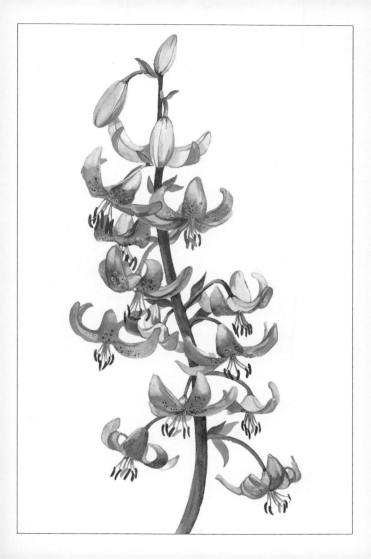

Lilium

Turk's Cap Lily
(L. superbum)
(Family: *Liliaceae*)

This is an especially spectacular wild lily found in wetland meadows and along woodland edges. Its nodding flowers, recurved petals and colored sepals distinguish this species from other lilies in the wild. Six brown anthers within each bloom tip back and forth like tiny see-saws at the ends of the stamen filaments. The common name comes from the resemblance of the flower to the turbans worn by Turkish rulers in the past. The lily can be found from New England to Georgia and as far west as Minnesota.

LINARIA

TOADFLAX
BUTTER AND EGGS
(L. vulgaris)
(Family: *Scrophulariaceae*)

❦

The spike-like masses of linaria's two-toned yellow-orange flowers resemble a small version of the garden snapdragon, to which they are related. The orange patch on the lower lip of the petals serves as a honey guide for insect pollinators, especially bumblebees. Nectar collects in the long spur which can be easily reached by moths with their long tongues. In Germany the flowers are used for making yellow dyes. Linaria is commonly found in dry open habitats such as fields and roadsides. Toads are said to enjoy the shade beneath its leaves, but the common name toadflax may come from a misreading, the Latin for "useful" having been taken for the word for "toad." In fact, the plant has been used in folk medicine to cure everything from boils to jaundice.

Lotus

Birdsfoot Trefoil
Bacon and Eggs
(L. corniculatus)
(Family: *Fabaceae*)

❧

Each pea-like flower of this lotus has five petals resembling an upright banner with two wings and a keel extending forward like the prow of a boat. The three most conspicuous leaves are somewhat clover-like. Fruiting pods are arranged in the shape of a bird's foot; from this formation comes one of the common names. Not to be outdone, some English countrypeople call it Fingers and Thumbs.

LYCHNIS

RAGGED ROBIN
(L. flos-cuculi)
(Family: *Caryophyllaceae*)

The common name Ragged Robin probably makes
reference to the medieval English bandit Robin Hood,
the adjective "ragged" describing the shredded,
ribbony look of the petals. The flowers are usually
colored a deep pink, though a white variety also
exists. Pairs of long, lance-like leaves ascend the
main stems, decreasing in size as they approach the
top. The plant is widespread from late spring to
midsummer, appearing in the clearings, meadows,
moors and pastures of Europe and northeastern
North America. An old English poem describes its
habitat more succinctly: "Poor Ragged Robin
blossoms in the haie."

LYCHNIS

WHITE CAMPION
EVENING LYCHNIS
(L. alba)
(Family: *Caryophyllaceae*)

❧

This is a densely hairy, opposite-leaved perennial with fragrant blossoms that open towards evening. Then, they exude a penetrating fragrance. Moths are common pollinators. The flowers are either male or female and are borne on separate plants. The calyx is somewhat inflated like the bladder campion. Both are members of the pink family and are related to the Deptford pink.

Lythrum

Purple Loosestrife
Spiked Willow-herb
Long Purples
Spiked Loosestrife
(L. salicaria)
(Family: *Lythraceae*)

In large numbers, the magenta flowers of purple loosestrife can provide a striking spectacle in wet meadows or marshes. Loosestrife has become such an aggressive alien in parts of the northeastern United States that there is concern that native wetland species will be crowded out. The plant responds well to cultivation and makes an attractive addition to any perennial garden. And it has had endless uses in folk medicine and custom. The ancients reportedly strung garlands of it around the necks of plowing oxen, to make them docile in the fields. The plants have been burned as an insect repellant, and extracts from them were once used to color hair blond. A drug derived from loosestrife is still used today in the treatment of amoebic dysentery.

MALVA

MUSK MALLOW
(M. moschata)
(Family: *Malvaceae*)

Related to the garden hollyhock, this plant can be
found along roadsides and in grassy or bushy places.
Its flower petals have deep pink veins. Its leaves are
deeply divided into narrow segments, and when they
are crushed, give off a delicate musky odor. The
great English gardener William Robinson
recommended it as a charming plant
for the wild garden.

MENYANTHES

BOGBEAN BUCKBEAN
(M. trifoliata)
(Family: *Menyanthaceae*)

Among the most beautiful of marsh plants, buckbean sends up tall stems adorned all along their lengths with lovely white and red flowers. Each has hairy nodes along the inside of its petals, lending the whole bloom a slightly unearthly quality. Found in bogs, marshes and on the edges of lakes and ponds, buckbean blooms from late spring to late summer. Even today, herbal doctors use it in the treatment of colds and fevers. In olden days, it was also used to cure scurvy and, as one authority put it, to treat "hot rotten agues."

MYOSOTIS

WATER FORGET-ME-NOT

MOUSE-EAR

SCORPION GRASS

(M. scorpioides)

(Family: *Boranginaceae*)

~

A native of Europe and Asia, this plant has escaped from American gardens and is now frequently found along streams and in marshes. The tiny blue tubular flowers are marked with a yellow ring near the center. The blooms occur in a tightly coiled cluster resembling a coiled scorpion's tail, thus the botanical designation "scorpioid cyme" for this distinctive arrangement of flowers.

NEPETA

CATNIP

(N. cataria)

(Family: *Lamiaceae*)

~

This plant attracts and pleases cats. It is now known that it also contains a chemical, nepeta lactone, which repels insects. Whether this is the chemical that gives catnip its unique effect on cats is not known. Catnip is thought to have originally come to America from Asia by way of Europe. The soft whitish hairs on stems and foliage help to identify this interesting mint.

PRUNELLA

SELF-HEAL
(P. vulgaris)
(Family: *Lamiaceae*)

~

Self-heal is a common, low-growing mint with a
square stem and a tight, elongated cluster of small,
irregularly shaped flowers. Mostly pollinated by
bumblebees, this species is thought to be native to
both North America and Europe. It can be found
in fields and lawns and along roadsides. As a
folk remedy, it is reported to heal wounds
and relieve fevers.

POTENTILLA

SULPHUR CINQUEFOIL
ROUGH-FRUITED CINQUEFOIL
(R. recta)
(Family: *Rosaceae*)

❥

An attractive member of the rose family, this cinquefoil makes a broad, simple flower whose color bleeds from sulphur-yellow to cream. Each bloom has a lovely nest of stamens at its heart, and the flowers appear in spare clusters on long, hairy stems. In reduced form, the Sulphur Cinquefoil shares some of the elegance of the cultivated rugosa roses. It grows in dry fields and along roadsides from late spring through high summer. Originally introduced from Central Europe, it is found naturalized in England and in quantities in Eastern and Mid-western North America. Nebraska farmers loathe it as a weed in their pastures.

PAPAVER

CORN POPPY
COQUELICOT
(P. rhoeas)
(Family: *Papaveraceae*)

~

The gardener will often plant bright, low-growing flowers among a bed of taller white flowers, for the lovely pattern thus formed. Nature's version of the practice is a field of wheat underlain with these scarlet poppies. The corn poppy is one of Europe's showiest wild flowers, especially in fields and other open places. It has been introduced into the United States where it is found around rubbish dumps and sometimes in fields. It is poisonous to livestock. The petals have been used to make red ink. The French name *Coquelicot* means "wild poppy."

OENOTHERA

EVENING PRIMROSE
(O. biennis)
(Family: *Onagraceae*)

As the common name implies, these flowers suddenly open in the evening and usually close by noon. For this reason, they are also known as Evening Star. The flowers have four petals and eight prominent stamens. The pollen is connected by cobwebby threads which make it easier for moths to transport. As a biennial it takes two years to flower, and then the plant dies. The cooked root can be eaten and resembles parsnip, but it must be collected at the right time. If taken too early or late it has a peppery taste. The oil of evening primrose has recently appeared as a cosmetic. Taken in pill form, it is said to help prevent aging of the skin.

RANUNCULUS

BULBOUS BUTTERCUP
(R. bulbosus)
(Family: *Ranunculaceae*)

This is one of several showy Old World buttercups.
The distinctively waxy texture of the shiny yellow
petals is the result of a special layer of cells found
just beneath the surface. This species is recognized
by its bulbous base or root. Common in fields and
meadows, it is poisonous to livestock. It has been
used in poultices to help heal rashes, but the
herbalist Gerard warned against careless use of the
Ranunculus in herbal medicine, for, as he put it,
"they are of a most violent force." Surprisingly to
some, the buttercups are not native to Europe: they
were brought back from Turkey and the Levant by
returning Crusaders.

Rosa

PRICKLY ROSE
ALBERTA ROSE
(R. acicularis)
(Family: *Rosaceae*)

Few flowers are as hardy or as widely distributed as
the prickly rose. Its lovely, solitary rose-pink
blossoms appear on a dense and very spiny bush
that grows up to about 4 feet (1.2 meters) high. And
the plant bears very pretty, pear-shaped red hips,
once the flowers are gone. Its range covers the whole
northern third of the United States and all of
Canada, from the Adirondacks of New York to the
province of New Brunswick. It also grows wild in the
mountains of Mongolia, the Kuriles and Japan. Its
hardiness has won it the nickname arctic rose, and it
is the provincial flower of Alberta. The prickly rose
has been naturalized in Britain since early in the
nineteenth-century.

SAGITTARIA

ARROWHEAD

(S. sagittifolia)
(Family: *Alismataceae*)

This is an aquatic plant with arrow-shaped leaves and whorls of white flowers, each accentuated with a dark violet basal patch. The upper flowers are male, and the lower ones are female. Arrowhead is typically found in still or slow-moving water throughout Europe. There are also numerous species of *Sagittaria* in North America. Their leaves have given them another nickname: Adder's Tongue.

SAPONARIA

BOUNCING BET
SOAPWORT
(S. officinalis)
(Family: *Caryophyllaceae*)

~

Bouncing Bet is a showy white or pink phlox-like fragrant flower that has come to America from Europe. The petals are scalloped with small appendages. This plant may be used for washing hands as it contains a soap-like substance (saponins) which lathers when the foliage is crushed. One of the common names, Bouncing Bet, refers to the appearance of a washerwoman, Betty, using an old-fashioned washing board.

SILENE

BLADDER CAMPION
(S. cucubalus)
(Family: *Caryophyllaceae*)

❦

The balloon-like calyx veined in green is the distinctive feature of this sun-loving perennial found in open fields. Its five petals are so deeply lobed that they often appear to number ten. The young tender shoots may be used as a potherb or boiled to make a soup similar to spinach puree.

TANACETUM

COMMON TANSY
(T. vulgare)
(Family: *Asteraceae*)

~

The flat-topped clusters of the tansy's button-like
heads are composed of many tiny flowers but lack
the typical collar of strap-like flowers, a characteristic
of tansy's relative, the daisies. The name of this
highly aromatic plant comes from Old French
tonesie, derived from the Greek word *athanasia,*
meaning immortality. In ancient times, it was
wrapped in winding sheets and rubbed on corpses,
perhaps to insure them a place in the afterlife. The
plant has been useful in folk medicine for many of
man's ills. A tea brewed from its leaves has been
used for curing aches and pains.

TRICHOSTEMA

BLUE CURLS
(T. dichotomum)
(Family: *Lamiaceae*)

~

The name Blue Curls refers to the extraordinarily long, curled stamens that form beautiful curves far beyond the petals of this two-lipped flower. It is a low-growing annual found in dry open sandy areas and along roadsides. In California, it grows much taller. There, this attractive member of the mint family is valued also for its attractiveness to bees.

TRIFOLIUM

RABBIT-FOOT CLOVER
(T. arvense)
(Family: *Fabaceae*)

The elongated flowering heads of this clover resemble
the furry feet of rabbits. This furry appearance
comes from tiny hairs on the sepals of the small,
greenish-white flowers. A low-growing annual, it is
often found in open fields or on bare soil areas. As a
member of the Pea family, it has tripartite and
clover-like leaves.

TRIFOLIUM

RED CLOVER
(T. pratense)
(Family: *Fabaceae*)

This is an important forage plant on both sides of
the Atlantic, especially where the spring climate is
cool. It, like other legumes, has the ability to fix
atmospheric nitrogen, a process which occurs in tiny
nodules on the roots. If you examine a red clover,
wash the soil from its roots and study these valuable
structures. Red clover and other related legumes, like
alfalfa, serve as important cover crops and improve
soil fertility. Trifolium means three-leaved, and
during medieval times, the triple sprigs were valued
as a charm against witches.

TRILLIUM

LARGE-FLOWERING TRILLIUM
(T. grandiflorum)
(Family: *Liliaceae*)

This is a large-flowered trillium that often finds its way into wildflower gardens. The three waxy white petals are larger than the three outer green sepals and turn pink with age. It can be found in rich woods from Missouri to Minnesota and northward into Canada. This trillium is the provincial flower of Ontario.

Verbascum

Common Mullein
(V. thapsus)
(Family: *Scrophulariaceae*)

❧

This common stout biennial, frequently found in waste places, banks and clearings, can attain a height of 8 feet (2.4 meters). Its rosette of velvety hairy leaves and its tightly packed spike of slightly asymmetrical yellow flowers are its distinguishing features. Roman soldiers are known to have used the flowering stalks for torches after dipping them in grease. The woolly leaves have been used for tea, wicks, and as padding to keep feet warm. Before rouge, women used the leaves to redden cheeks by rubbing the fuzzy leaf on the skin and irritating it. The masses of delicate, branched leaf hairs of the plant are most unusual and well worth examining with a hand lens.

VICIA

COW VETCH
BLUE VETCH
(V. cracca)
(Family: *Fabaceae*)

❦

This is a graceful vine with tendrils and gray-green
compound leaves (those having many leaflets on
each leaf). Related to both the common garden and
sweet pea, vicia is frequently found in fields and
along roadsides. Its many small, pea-like blossoms
are aggregated in one-sided, crowded spikes. Its
fruits resemble miniature peapods. As a legume
it makes a good cover crop and enriches the
soil with nitrogen.

WILDFLOWER GLOSSARY

ALTERNATE
Having one leaf at every stem node, pointing in different directions.

ANNUAL
A plant that completes its life cycle (germinates, grows, flowers, fruits and dies) within a single year or growing season.

ANTHER
The sac-like, upper part of the stamen where pollen is produced. When the anther breaks, wind or insects carry pollen to the tip of the pistil.

APPENDAGE
Any subsidiary part attached to another part.

AXIL
The angle formed where a leaf or branch diverges from the stem or axis to which it is attached.

BASAL LEAVES
Leaves that grow at the base of the stem.

BEARDED
Bearing hairs, either stiff or elongated.

BISEXUAL
Said of flowers having both stamens (male) and pistils (female) on a single flower.

BLADE
The flat part of a sepal, petal or leaf.

BRACT
A small, leaf-like, occasionally brightly colored organ usually located at the base of the flower.

BULB
A subterranean organ made up of tightly packed leaves.

CALYX
The collective term for the sepals, which form the outer whorl of the flower.

CAPSULE
A dry fruit that releases its seed through slits or pores.

CARPEL
The female organ of a flower, comprised of stigma, style and ovary.

COMPOUND
Referring to a leaf divided into smaller leaflets arranged either in two rows (pinnate) or radially, like a fan (palmate).

COROLLA
The collective term for the petals which form the inner whorl of the flower.

CORYMB
A panicle all of whose flowers are arranged roughly along the same plane.

CYME
A wide, usually branching cluster of flowers, in which a bloom appears at the end of each stalk.

DISK FLOWER
The tiny tubular flowers at the center of a tight flower head, as in daisies.

DISTURBED SITE
Any area of ground that has previously been cleared or excavated for human purposes.

DIVIDED
Referring to a deeply cut leaf, the cleft not reaching to the central vein.

EXOTIC
Of plants that are not native; from another region.

FILAMENT
The stalk connected to the anther in a stamen.

HEAD
A tight cluster of flowers, each on a very short stalk or even stalkless.

HERBACEOUS
A soft-stemmed plant; not woody.

HIP
The fruit of a rose.

LEAFLET
Each leaf-like part of a compound leaf.

LEGUME
A fruit developed from a single ovary, usually splitting at maturity into two valves, as in the Pea family.

LIP
The lower petal of asymmetrical flowers, as in orchids.

LOBED
Indented, but not divided into separate parts.

OPPOSITE
Having a pair of leaves at each stem node.

OVARY
The swollen, lower portion of the pistil that produces tiny ovules, which following fertilization, develop into seeds.

OVATE
In the shape of an egg, pointed at the top.

PALMATE
Lobed like the fingers of a hand.

PERENNIAL
A plant that lasts through more than two growing seasons.

PERIANTH
A flower's nonsexual, outer parts, either as a tube or as calyx and corolla.

PETAL
The inner segments of the perianth; basic units of the corolla, surrounding the flower's reproductive organs.

PINNATE
Said of leaves appearing in opposite pairs along a central stalk, in the manner of a feather.

PISTIL
The female organ of a flower, consisting of stigma, style and ovary.

POLLEN
Spores produced in the anthers, carrying the male reproductive elements.

RACEME
An elongated flower branch with stalked flowers.

RAY FLOWER
In the Daisy family, the bilaterally symmetrical flowers around the edge of the head; each flower resembles a petal.

REFLEXED
Term used to describe leaves and petals that bend backwards.

RHIZOME
A creeping underground rootstock which sprouts each year anew.

ROSETTE
A dense, circular cluster of leaves usually appearing at the base of a stem; it often seems to grow right out of the ground.

RUGOSE
Wrinkled.

RUNNER
A stem that grows along the ground, sending out new roots and plants at the nodes or tip.

SAC
A bag-shaped structure in a plant.

SCALLOPED
Having shallow, rounded projections.

SCORPIOID
A coiled flower cluster with the flowers usually appearing on one side of the stem.

SEPAL
Part of the calyx of a flower, usually green, but sometimes brightly colored; hence, they are sometimes mistaken for petals where true petals are absent.

SIMPLE
Said of a leaf with no divisions in the blade.

SPADIX
A thick spike of tiny flowers, usually enclosed in a spathe.

SPIKE
An elongated flower branch with stalkless flowers.

SPUR
A hollow, slender projection from the flower base.

STAMEN
The male pollen-producing organ of a flower, consisting of a filament topped by an anther.

STANDARD
The upper petal, or banner, of members of the Pea family; the iris petal.

STIGMA
The usually divided or club-shaped tip of the pistil, which receives pollen.

STYLE
The part of the pistil which joins the ovary to the stigma.

TAPROOT
The strongly developed central root of a plant, usually extending straight down.

TENDRIL
A coiling structure that helps support climbing plants.

TUBER
The fleshy part of a subterranean stem, for storage of nutrients.

UMBEL
A flower cluster whose individuals have stalks growing from a single point.

WHORL
At a stem node, a circle of leaves, branches or flowers.

WOODY
Said of plants with wooden, as opposed to fleshy, stems; not herbaceous.

WILDFLOWERS
IN THE GARDEN

While many of the flowers in this book are at their best in the wild, a number of them make fine additions to the wild, or naturalistic, garden.

Aquilegia

The columbines are difficult to grow. They tend to look flabby in the garden, and they interbreed easily, producing unsightly offspring. But if you can grow true seed of *A. canadensis* for your rock garden, you will have a lovely plant indeed. Plant it in clumps, preferably in full sun, in rocky soil.

Calla

"*Calla palustris* is a beautiful bog plant, and nothing gives a better effect creeping over rich, soft, boggy ground." So said William Robinson, the father of wild gardening, and generations of gardeners have followed his advice. Plant it in the wettest part of the bog garden, and give it a modicum of sun. Propagate it by dividing the rootstock or by sprouting the berries.

Campanula

Growing in the grass, in the rock garden or in a flower border, *C. rotundifolia* gives a lovely effect. Easy to grow from seed or by division, this campanula has only one problem: it may become rampant.

Chelidonium

The celandine (*Chelidonium majus*) is by no means a common flower in the woodland garden, but it looks uncommonly well there, its groups of small yellow flowers standing out of the rich woodland soil. It is easy to grow.

Cornus

Bunchberry (*C. canadensis*) is a charming plant that, once established, will spread into a carpet that is lovely to look at all season long. It prefers moist, acid soils in the woodland or peat garden, but it must be given plenty of sun.

Coronilla

Many of the plants of this genus make attractive garden plants in groups on grassy banks and rocky ground. *C. varia* is beautiful indeed, but plant it only in the rockiest places and well isolated from the rest of the garden; otherwise, it will spread everywhere.

Cypripedium

Cypripediums can be difficult to grow in the garden, though surpassingly lovely. Fortunately, *C. calceolus* is among the easiest. It may grow in rich garden earth, but the best idea is to give it a limy soil enriched with leaf mold. Make sure it has plenty of shade, by planting taller bushes to protect it, if necessary.

Daucus

Queen-Anne's Lace (*D. carota*) is virtually a symbol of the wild and is easy to grow. It graces many a woodland bouquet or flower arrangement in late summer.

Epilobium

Fireweed (*E. angustifolium*) is a spectacular flower. When planted in masses, it can be seen from quite far off. Place it in open woodland settings, where its rampant growth will not disturb the rest of the garden.

Habenaria

The orchids of this genus are difficult to grow, and they seldom last more than a season or two. Still, they are so beautiful that it is worth a try, if you have a bog or woodland site. Grow them in half-shade in a moist, peaty soil.

Iris

All the irises make gardens shine, but Yellow Flag (*I. pseudacoris*) gives a specially wild and pleasant effect. They should be planted in a sunny location with limy soil.

Lilium

William Robinson recommends the planting of various species of the lilies as accent plants in the rhododendron garden. *L. superbum* is particularly recommended for the bog or woodland garden.

Lythrum

Purple loosestrife (*L. salicaria*) adapts very well to the cultivated perennial garden. It looks especially well, besides, gracing the edge of a pond. Try the variety called *L. roseum superbum*.

Malva

M. moschata is a wonderful, airy flower for banks and woodland clearings. It produces flowers through most of the summer. Propagate by seed or by root cuttings.

Oenothera

Handsome and hardy, the evening primrose (*O. biennis*) will grow in almost any soil. Plant it out of the way of the rest of the garden, however, as it spreads very freely.

Sagittaria

Arrowhead grows happily in water gardens or along the margins of ponds. Propagate by seeds or by root division.

Saponaria

Soapwort (*S. officinalis*) was suggested by William Robinson for the rock or heath garden, but he reports no results.

Trillium

The trillium pictured in this volume is the most beautiful of a wide genus. Plant it in masses in a shady area of moist soil enriched with leaf mold. Propagate by seed or by rhizomes.

Vicia

Use slender supports to train blue vetch (*V. cracca*) as a border plant. By the time the plant flowers, the supports should be well covered.